www.raintreepublishers.co.uk
Visit our website to find out more information about Raintree books.

**To order:**
☎ Phone 0845 6044371
📄 Fax +44 (0) 1865 312263
✉ Email myorders@raintreepublishers.co.uk

Customers from outside the UK please telephone +44 1865 312262

Raintree is an imprint of Capstone Global Library Limited, a company incorporated in England and Wales having its registered office at 7 Pilgrim Street, London, EC4V 6LB - Registered company number: 6695582

First published by Raintree in 2013
The moral rights of the proprietor have been asserted.

Originally published by DC Comics in the U.S. in single magazine form as Superman Adventures #4.
Copyright © 2012 DC Comics. All Rights Reserved.

Ashley C. Andersen Zantop *Publisher*
Michael Dahl *Editorial Director*
Donald Lemke & Sean Tulien *Editors*
Heather Kindseth *Creative Director*
Bob Lentz *Designer*
Kathy McColley *Production Specialist*

*DC COMICS*
Mike McAvennie *Original U.S. Editor*
Bruce Timm *Cover Artist*

ISBN 978 1 406 25402 0
16 15 14 13 12
10 9 8 7 6 5 4 3 2 1
Printed and bound in China by Nordica.
0512/CA21200799
*British Library Cataloguing in Publication Data*
A full catalogue record for this book is available from the British Library.

# SUPERMAN ADVENTURES

## Eye to Eye

Scott McCloud...................... writer
Rick Burchett ...................penciller
Terry Austin .......................... inker
Marie Severin .................... colorist
Lois Buhalis........................ letterer

Superman created by
Jerry Siegel & Joe Shuster

NOBODY CALLS ME A COWARD AND GETS AWAY WITH IT! WHO DOES HE THINK HE IS?

I DON'T HAVE TO PUT UP WITH THIS KIND OF ABUSE!

COWARD? WHO CALLED YOU A COWARD, JIMMY?

MR. WHITE DID. MAYBE NOT IN SO MANY WORDS, BUT...

I'M SURE HE DIDN'T MEAN--

OH, HE MEANT IT, ALL RIGHT.

HE'S PROBABLY RIGHT. I WISH I WAS MORE LIKE SUPERMAN.

WELL... I'D HARDLY CALL SUPERMAN BRAVE.

WHEN YOU'RE AS STRONG AS SUPERMAN, YOU DON'T HAVE TO BE BRAVE.

YOU WANT TO SEE REAL COURAGE, LOOK AT SOMEONE LIKE LOIS.

SHE'S AS VULNERABLE AS YOU OR ME, BUT STILL SHE GOES LOOKING FOR TROUBLE AGAIN AND AGAIN.

LISTEN, YOU LITTLE WEASEL, IF YOU DON'T COME CLEAN WITH ME, I'M GONNA COME DOWN TO CITY HALL AND PUNCH YOUR LIGHTS OUT!

BRAVERY ISN'T ABOUT HAVING NO FEAR, JIMMY. BRAVERY IS ABOUT FACING YOUR FEARS.

14

BOOM! BOOM! BOOM! BO

THERE HE GOES!

WOW!

BOOM! BOOM!

BOOM!

SNAP!

WOW! WHAT A SNAPSHOT, huh, KID?

"SNAPSHOT"? HE THINKS I'M JUST ANOTHER TOURIST!

DON'T WASTE YOUR TIME, JIMMY! LET'S GET A PIECE OF THIS ACTION!

TAXI!

# CREATORS

## SCOTT McCLOUD WRITER

Scott McCloud is an acclaimed comics creator and author whose best-known work is the graphic novel *Understanding Comics*. His work also includes the science-fiction adventure series *Zot!*, a 12-issue run of *Superman Adventures* and much more. Scott is the creator of the "24 Hour Comic," and frequently lectures on comics theory.

## RICK BURCHETT PENCILLER

Rick Burchett has worked as a comics artist for more than 25 years. He has received the comics industry's Eisner Award three times, Spain's Haxtur Award, and he has been nominated for England's Eagle Award. Rick lives with his wife and two sons in Missouri, USA.

## TERRY AUSTIN INKER

Throughout his career, inker Terry Austin has received dozens of awards for his work on high-profile comics for DC Comics and Marvel, such as *The Uncanny X-Men, Doctor Strange, Justice League America, Green Lantern,* and *Superman Adventures.* He lives in New York, USA.

# GLOSSARY

**affection** great liking for someone or something

**arranged** made plans for something to happen

**breach** to break through something or make a hole in something

**complex** building or group of buildings housing related units

**convenient** if something is convenient, it is useful or easy to use

**coward** someone who is easily scared and runs away from frightening situations

**dispatch** to send something or somebody off

**mechanical** to do with machines or tools, or operated by machinery

**negotiator** someone who bargains or discusses something so that two parties can come to an agreement

**Polaroid** brand of camera that produces developed pictures

**reversible** if something is reversible, it is able to be returned to its original condition

**surrender** to give up, or admit that you are beaten

**vulnerable** able to be damaged

# SUPERMAN GLOSSARY

**Clark Kent:** Superman's alter ego, Clark Kent, is a reporter for the *Daily Planet* newspaper and was raised by Ma and Pa Kent. No one knows he is Superman except for his adopted parents, the Kents.

**The Daily Planet:** the city of Metropolis's biggest and most read newspaper. Clark, Lois, Jimmy, and Perry all work for the *Daily Planet*.

**Invulnerability:** Superman's invulnerability makes him impervious to harm. Almost nothing can hurt him -- except for Kryptonite, a radioactive rock from his home planet, Krypton.

**Jimmy Olsen:** Jimmy is a cub reporter and photographer. He is also a friend to Lois and Clark.

**Lex Luthor:** Lex believes Superman is a threat to Earth and must be stopped. He will do anything it takes to bring the Man of Steel to his knees.

**Lois Lane:** like Clark Kent, Lois is a reporter at the *Daily Planet* newspaper. She is also one of Clark's best friends.

**Metropolis:** the city where Clark Kent (Superman) lives.

**S.T.A.R. Labs:** a research center in Metropolis, where scientists make high-tech tools and devices for Superman and other heroes.

# VISUAL QUESTIONS & PROMPTS

**1** Why do these two crooks change their minds? What reasons would they have for lying about working for Lex?

BUT, BUT, UH...

...UH...

UH...RIGHT.

1

**2** Superman uses several of his superpowers in this story as seen in the panel below. Identify three other panels in which Superman uses one of his superpowers.

**3** Why would Lex not want the criminals to come to LexCorp? Why might that be bad for him?

2

TELL THEM TO STOP HIM. IF THEY CAN'T STOP HIM, STOP *THEM!*

HOSE FOOLS UST NOT LEAD HIM HERE.

3

**4** In the panel below, what does Superman mean by saying the false alarm and security breach happening at the same time was convenient? Explain your answer.

I DON'T KNOW HOW THEY DID IT, SUPERMAN. THERE WERE AT LEAST A *DOZEN* OF US WORKING THE NIGHT SHIFT.

UNFORTUNATELY, THERE WAS A *FALSE ALARM* ON THE OTHER SIDE OF THE COMPLEX WHEN IT HAPPENED, SO SECURITY WAS NOWHERE NEAR THE BREACH.

HOW CONVENIENT.

S.T.A.R. LABS, 10:27 PM.

**5** Of all the characters in this comic book, who do you think was the most brave and the least brave? Why?

HE'S PROBABLY RIGHT. I WISH I WAS MORE LIKE SUPERMAN.

WELL... I'D HARDLY CALL SUPERMAN *BRAVE*.

WHEN YOU'RE AS STRONG AS SUPERMAN, YOU DON'T *HAVE* TO BE BRAVE.

I'M *FINE*, JIMMY. SUPERMAN, THEY'RE *GETTING AWAY!*

PAF!

PAF!